ARE WE NEARLY THERE YET?

WRITTEN BY ALISON BREWIS

ILLUSTRATED BY JENNY BRAKE

Two excited children are wriggling in the car.

They're driving down to Granny's, it's really really far!

They're waiting to see Granny and eat an Easter lunch,

but most of all they're waiting for some chocolate eggs to munch!

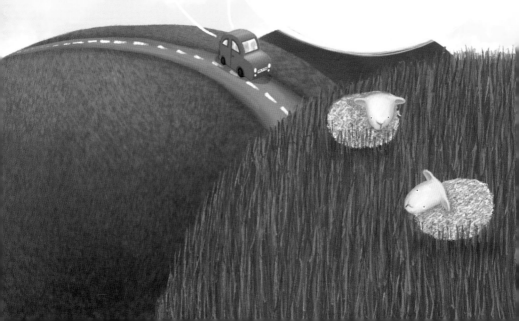

"Just a little LONGER,
and it will all be great.
I'll tell the Easter story,
so LISTEN while you wait..."

Jesus' disciples had followed him about.

They saw him calm a mighty storm with just a single shout.

He fed 5000 people with just some fish and bread,

"INCREDIBLE! AMAZING!"

That's what the people said.

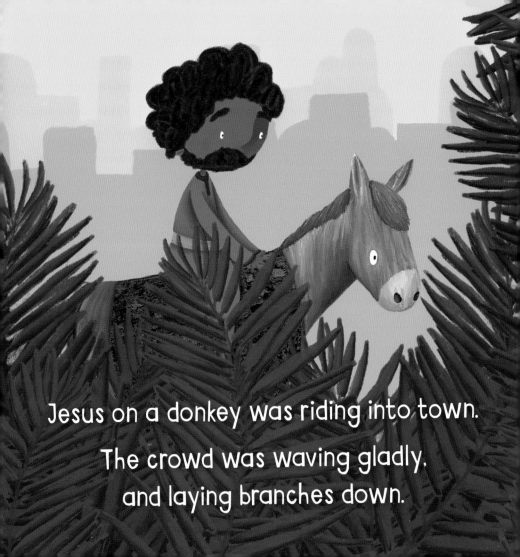

Jesus on a donkey was riding into town.
The crowd was waving gladly,
and laying branches down.

They shouted, "JESUS SAVE US!"

And, "JESUS IS THE KING!"

And Jesus' disciples all turned and said to him...

Just a few days
later, some soldiers
came along,

and Jesus' disciples
thought the plan
was going wrong.

Jesus was arrested, and on a cross he died.

His friends were sad and worried, they ran away and cried.

Now Jesus died on Friday,
but when Sunday came around,

the tomb was broken open, an
earthquake SHOOK the ground.

"Are we nearly there yet?
Well, NOW we understand.

Dying to forgive us was
EXACTLY what you'd planned.

We thought we'd cry forever,
but it was worth the wait.

Now Jesus is the REAL KING,
it's time to celebrate!"

TAKING IT FURTHER

If you'd like to read the stories about Jesus that are
mentioned in this poem, then you can look them up in the Bible.

You can find Jesus calming the storm in Luke 8:22-25.

Jesus feeds 5000 people in John 6:1-14.

Jesus rides into Jerusalem on a donkey in John 12:12-15.

John 19:16-30 tells you about Jesus' death.

You can find Jesus' resurrection in John 20:1-18.

TALKING...

You can discuss the themes raised in the story with your children to reinforce their learning and to help them think about what happened to Jesus at Easter. Here are some ideas...

Talk about the story (or read it again!) when you're on a long journey. How did the children in the story feel at the beginning of the book? Do you think that's what Jesus' friends felt like too? How did everyone feel at the end of the story?

Talk about things that don't turn out as you expect – an unexpected birthday present or a book or film with a

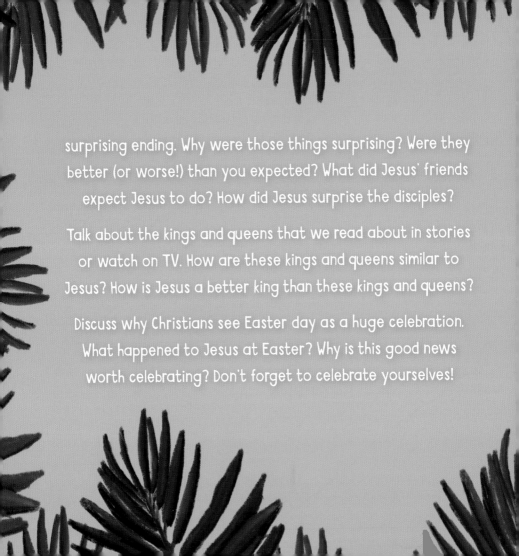

surprising ending. Why were those things surprising? Were they better (or worse!) than you expected? What did Jesus' friends expect Jesus to do? How did Jesus surprise the disciples?

Talk about the kings and queens that we read about in stories or watch on TV. How are these kings and queens similar to Jesus? How is Jesus a better king than these kings and queens?

Discuss why Christians see Easter day as a huge celebration. What happened to Jesus at Easter? Why is this good news worth celebrating? Don't forget to celebrate yourselves!

PLAYING...

If you're feeling creative, why not continue to explore the Easter story through play? While you play you can remind your child of Jesus' friends and their long wait.

Play an imaginary long journey game. Pack a bag and dress for a journey before 'hiking' around the house. As you travel around the house ask, "Are we nearly there yet?" You could have a surprise snack when you reach the mountain peak/top of the stairs!

Bake something with a delicious surprise to enjoy together – cakes, cookies or doughnuts with a hidden jammy centre.

Enjoy breaking apart a piñata together. Emphasize that although you have to be patient and wait for the treats to fall, you do get a delicious surprise in the end.

For Nicholas, Ana and Isabelle

Published by 10Publishing, a division of 10ofThose Limited.
ISBN 978-1-912373-55-0

Typeset by Diane Warnes.

10ofThose Limited, Unit C Tomlinson Road, Leyland, PR25 2DY
Email: info@10ofthose.com   Website: www.10ofthose.com